The Christmas Story

igloobooks
.com

Long ago, in Nazareth, a mother dove said
to her baby, "A very special time has come.
Fly with me, little one, and I will show you why."

The mother dove flew with her baby, over quiet, sleepy Nazareth. Suddenly, a dazzling light shone out from the windows of a little house.

Inside the house, the angel Gabriel had appeared. He spoke to a girl called Mary. "You will have a special baby boy," he said. "He is the son of God and you will call him Jesus."

Over many months, the little dove came to see
Mary and her husband, Joseph. One day, Joseph
said to Mary, "We must make a journey to Bethlehem."

Mary rode on a donkey and Joseph walked along the dusty path to Bethlehem. The little dove felt sorry for them. "They must be very tired," he thought.

In Bethlehem, the night had come, but all the
inns were full. There was nowhere to rest for Mary
and Joseph and everyone turned them away.

The very last innkeeper took pity on them.
"You can stay in my stable," he said. So, Mary and
Joseph went inside to settle down for the night.

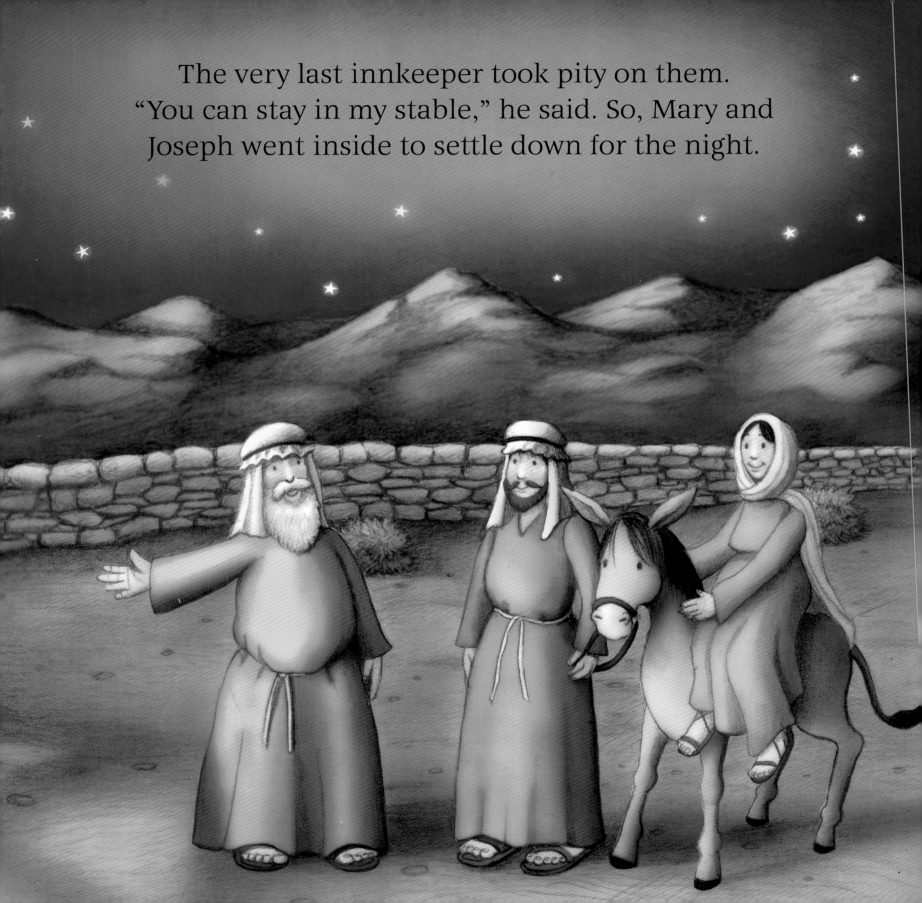

On a hill nearby, shepherds were tending their sheep, when an angel appeared to them. "Do not be afraid," he said. "For Jesus is born this night."

Far away in the east, three kings saw a star. "We must follow it," they said. "The star is a sign that Jesus is born. We will go to him this night."

The little dove saw the traveling kings, as they came near Bethlehem. They rode their camels and brought with them gifts of gold, frankincense and myrrh.

The shepherds and kings all gathered round to see Jesus in the manger. A great light shone over everyone and they were filled with joy.

The little dove knew that Jesus would
bring a time of peace and hope. Everyone rejoiced
at his holy birth, on this very special night.

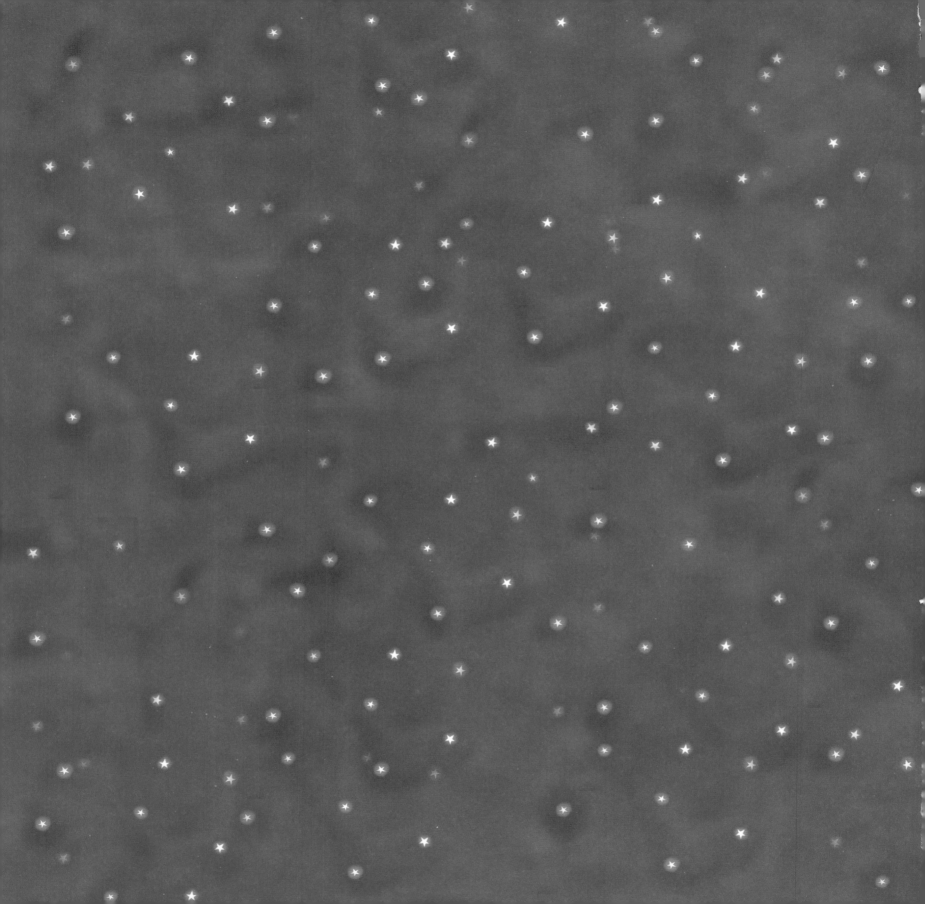